KAISER CHIEFS
Yours Truly, Angry Mob

All the songs from the album, arranged for piano, voice & guitar.

WISE PUBLICATIONS
part of The Music Sales Group

London/New York/Paris/Sydney/Copenhagen/Berlin/Madrid/Tokyo

Published by
Wise Publications
14-15 Berners Street, London, W1T 3LJ, UK.

Exclusive distributors:
Music Sales Limited
Distribution Centre, Newmarket Road,
Bury St Edmunds, Suffolk, IP33 3YB, UK.

Music Sales Pty Limited
120 Rothschild Avenue, Rosebery,
NSW 2018, Australia.

Order No. AM990132
ISBN 978-1-84772-033-7
This book © Copyright 2007 Wise Publications,
a division of Music Sales Limited.

Edited by Tom Farncombe.
Music arranged by Derek Jones.
Music processed by Paul Ewers Music Design.
Original sleeve art direction and design by Cally at antar.cc

Printed in the EU.

www.musicsales.com

Ruby

Words & Music by
Charlie Wilson, Nicholas Hodgson, Andrew White,
James Rix & Nicholas Baines

Could it be, could it be, that you're jok-ing with me,_____ and you don't real-ly see_____ you with me?_____

Electric guitar solo

The Angry Mob

Words & Music by
Charlie Wilson, Nicholas Hodgson, Andrew White,
James Rix & Nicholas Baines

Original key E♭ minor.

♩ = 124

1. I can prove a - ny - thing,_____ I'll make you ad - mit
2. You could choose a - ny - thing,_____ and you choose to lose
3. You could try a - ny - thing,_____ and no - one would know

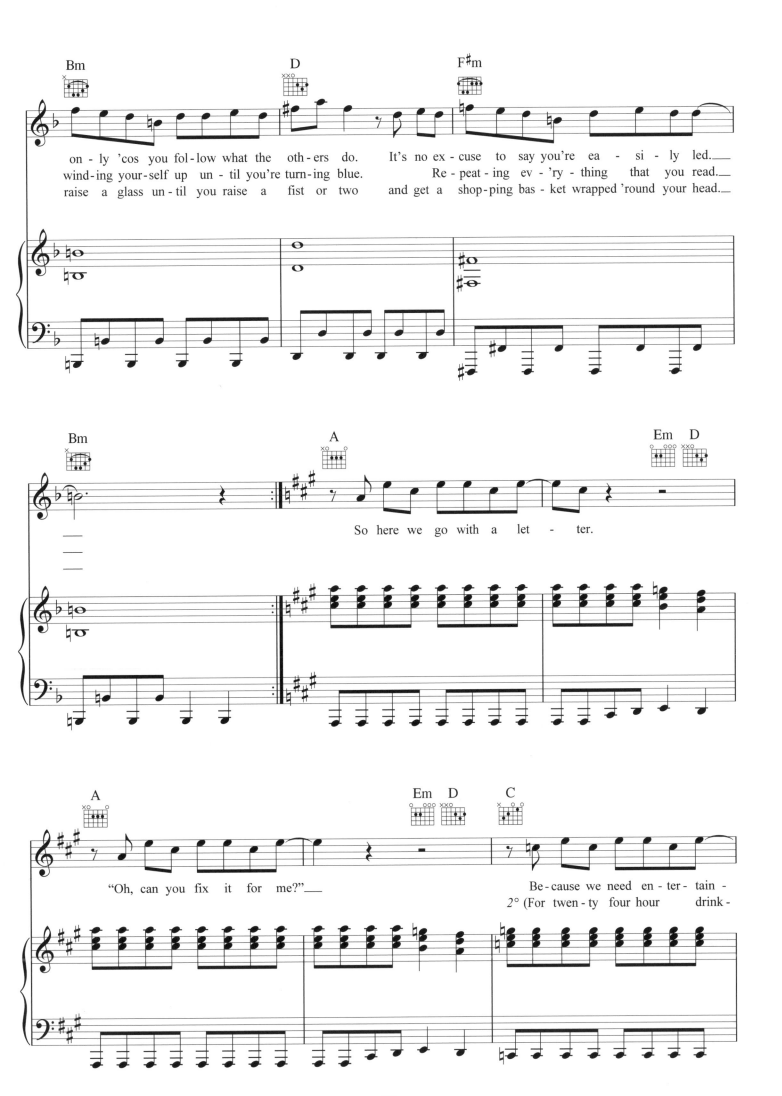

Heat Dies Down

Words & Music by
Charlie Wilson, Nicholas Hodgson, Andrew White,
James Rix & Nicholas Baines

Highroyds

Words & Music by
Charlie Wilson, Nicholas Hodgson, Andrew White,
James Rix & Nicholas Baines

Love's Not A Competition
(But I'm Winning)

Words & Music by
Charlie Wilson, Nicholas Hodgson, Andrew White,
James Rix & Nicholas Baines

Thank You Very Much

Words & Music by
Charlie Wilson, Nicholas Hodgson, Andrew White,
James Rix & Nicholas Baines

Did-n't want you to cause a fuss___ but it
Nev - er thought I would ex - pe - ri - ence this___ from the

feels al - right.___
o - ther side.___
So thank you ve - ry much,

that's real - ly nice to know

that you en -joyed the

show. And I want you___ to know___ when to go 'cos this

I Can Do It Without You

Words & Music by
Charlie Wilson, Nicholas Hodgson, Andrew White,
James Rix & Nicholas Baines

My Kind Of Guy

Words & Music by
Charlie Wilson, Nicholas Hodgson, Andrew White,
James Rix & Nicholas Baines

brakes.
chase.
fast,

Then a bi - cy - cle flips, crush-ing ribs, smash-ing hips. And he
You're a right piece of work All the flakes, go ber-serk, have you for-
there's a word to the wise, you should take my ad - vice, 'cause the

broke ev - 'ry bone in his face.
- got - ten how good they taste?
nice guys al - ways fin - ish last.

You're

my kind of guy 'cos I like your style, and you sound as hor-ri-ble as

me. And I don't mind if you're un-kind. You're re-mind-ing me of

To Coda

me.

Guitar

1.

2.

D.S. al Coda

And the

Everything Is Average Nowadays

Words & Music by
Charlie Wilson, Nicholas Hodgson, Andrew White,
James Rix & Nicholas Baines

Boxing Champ

Words & Music by
Charlie Wilson, Nicholas Hodgson, Andrew White,
James Rix & Nicholas Baines

We went to the youth_ club_ and we looked out of place._____

53

run a - way.___ At least I en - joy what I do to - day.___ And I thank you ve - ry

much that I do._____

Learnt My Lesson Well

Words & Music by
Charlie Wilson, Nicholas Hodgson, Andrew White,
James Rix & Nicholas Baines

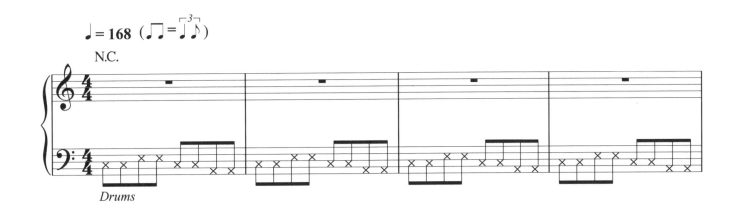

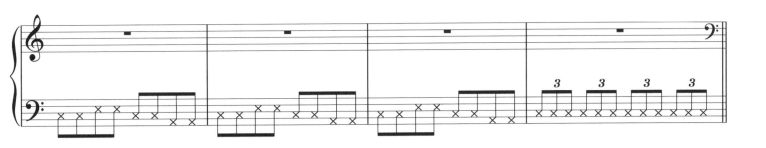

I'm just wait-ing for___ the man___ to come_ and go___ a-way.___
seems most sen-si-ble___ but not___ ex-act-ly what___ we'd like.___
I'm still wait-ing for___ the man___ to come_ with all___ my things._

Am7   D   Am7

What are you wait-ing for?   Get up off___

D   Gm7   C

___ your seat.   It's just se-ven days,___

Gm7   C   Am7

it feels like a week.___   What are you moan-

57

Try Your Best

Words & Music by
Charlie Wilson, Nicholas Hodgson, Andrew White,
James Rix & Nicholas Baines

try your best   and think a-bout_ it lat - er   or   you will   nev - er   know.__

— which   way   your   life   could   go,____   and you'll know when you   know.__

Know.

Retirement

Words & Music by
Charlie Wilson, Nicholas Hodgson, Andrew White,
James Rix & Nicholas Baines

1. There are ma-ny things____ that I would be proud of____ if I'd on-ly in-vent-
2. There are ma-ny things____ that I know I could do____ if I'd on-ly have want-

- ed them, such as the wheel,____ the wash-ing ma-chine____ and the tum-ble dryer.____
- ed to, such as cre-ate____ the per-fect tone____ that ev-'ry one would ad-mire.____

68

3. Now my place in his-to-ry is sure-ly as-sured.__ I will be re-mem-bered here for ev-er more.__ A brand new pro-duct's in place__ and a po-ten-tial buy-er.__ Up-on this next trans-ac-